James L. Heaney.

Xmas. 1923.

Revised Edition

ALDINE READERS
BOOK TWO

BY

FRANK E. SPAULDING

Head of the Department of Education, Graduate School
Yale University
Formerly Superintendent of Schools, Cleveland
Minneapolis, Newton, and Passaic

AND

CATHERINE T. BRYCE

Assistant Professor of Elementary Education, Graduate School
Yale University
Formerly Assistant Superintendent of Schools, Cleveland and Minneapolis
and Supervisor of Primary Instruction, Newton and Passaic

ILLUSTRATED BY MARGARET ELY WEBB

NEW YORK
NEWSON & COMPANY

PREFACE

THIS second reader, like the two preceding books of the Aldine Series, combines material and method in such a way that the former does not suffer, while the latter gains by the combination. That is, the subject-matter of the book, both the text and the illustrations, is just as suitable and just as interesting as it could be made were there no such thing as method; indeed the sole sign of method, as one reads the book, is the parentheses about certain words preceding the stories. At the same time, this subject-matter, both the text and the illustrations, embodies in systematic arrangement the most effective principles of mastering the mechanics of reading.

Children who have read thoroughly the preceding books of this Series have acquired independence, the habit of self-reliance, and the power of self-help to such a degree that they will be able to master this book with little or no direct aid from the teacher. And when they have thus mastered this book, they will be good readers. That is, so far as the mechanics of reading is concerned, they will be able to read unaided anything which they can understand; so far as the subject-matter is concerned, they will be able to

3

understand from the printed page anything which they can understand through the spoken word. More than this, if the teacher has contributed her part, most such children will have realized the utility and tasted the real delights of reading to such an extent that they will continue to read of their own accord; most of them will also be good oral readers, reading with appropriate expression and genuine enthusiasm.

These statements are not mere predictions of the hoped-for results of untried theories; they are simple, unexaggerated expressions of facts which have been observed in the work of tens of thousands of children of a score of nationalities.

To secure such results a complete mastery and intelligent observation is necessary of the principles and plans described in the authors' *Manual for Teachers*, entitled "Learning to Read."

The authors gratefully acknowledge their indebtedness to Miss Marie Van Vorst for the use of "Three of us Know" and "The Sandman"; to Mrs. Emily Huntington Miller for "The Bluebird"; to Messrs. Houghton, Mifflin Co. for the use of the poem "Discontent," by Sarah Orne Jewett, and "Calling the Violet," by Lucy Larcom; to Messrs. Charles Scribner's Sons for "The Wind," by Robert Louis Stevenson; to Mrs. Lida Brown McMurry for "The Indian Mother's Lullaby."

CONTENTS

6

Out of Door Neighbors

WHY THE BIRDS SING DIFFERENT SONGS

learn	owl	(hush)	(love)
choose		thrush	dove

A TEACHER–PUPIL STORY

Teacher

Long, long ago, when the world was new, the owl, the crow, the jay, the robin, the thrush, and the dove sang the same song. They sang this song over and over so often that at last they grew tired of it and wished they could sing different songs.

Pupil

"My friends," said the robin one day, "let us all learn a new song."

"Good! good!" cried the other birds. "How

9

shall we learn new songs? Where shall we learn new songs?"

"Let us listen to all we hear today," said the thrush. "Let us choose the sweetest sound we hear and make it into a song."

"Good! good!" cried the other birds. "We will! We will!"

Then they all flew away to listen to the sweetest sound they could hear.

The owl was a lazy bird. He did not want to fly around and listen. So he flew away to the woods.

Teacher

He crept into a hollow tree and tried to go to sleep. But the wind began to blow and kept him awake.

Pupils

"Oo-oo-oo! Oo-oo-oo!" blew the wind.

"That is a good song," said the owl. "I will choose it for my song."

10

So he tried to sing it. But all he could say was, "Who! who! who!" And that is the owl's song to this day.

The crow and the blue-jay flew off together. Soon they saw a little girl and a little boy.

"What dear children," said the crow. "Let us fly down. I am sure we will learn a sweet song from them."

The crow and the blue-jay flew down to the children.

Teacher

But how can I tell you the rest of the sad story! They heard no sweet songs from the children. No, indeed! I'm sorry to say they were quarrelling and screaming at each other in harsh angry voices.

Pupils

The blue-jay and the crow learned to sing what the children said. That is why their songs are not sweet.

11

Now isn't that too bad!

The robin flew to Jack's house. Jack was a lazy boy. He did not like to get up in the morning. Every morning his mother had to call him again and again.

Just as the robin flew by, the mother called, "Get up, Jack! get up! get up! get up!"

"That is a good song for me," said the robin. "I'll sing it every morning and wake all the other birds."

Teacher

If you are awake early, about three o'clock, any bright spring morning, you will hear the robin sing, "Get up! get up!" for that is his song to this very day.

Pupils

The thrush flew into the meadow. A little brook ran through it.

"Oh, listen to the song of the brook," said the thrush. "How sweet it is! How happy it is! I will learn to sing it, too."

To this day the thrush sings the song of the happy brook.

The dove flew to a little house. A dear little baby was lying on the grass before the door.

13

"Goo! Goo!" crowed the happy baby. "Goo! Goo! Goo!"

"How sweet!" said the dove. "I know that is the sweetest sound in all the world. I will choose it for my song."

Then the dove flew off cooing, "Goo! coo! coo! goo!" and that is her song to this very day.

grasshopper   once   afraid

THE GRASSHOPPER AND THE DOVE

Once upon a time a dove saw a grasshopper on the ground.

"What a fat grasshopper," said the dove. "I will get him for my breakfast."

The dove flew down to the grass. The grasshopper did not try to run away. He was not a bit afraid of the dove.

"Good morning, friend dove," he said.

"What!" cried the dove. "Are you not afraid of me?"

"No," answered the grasshopper.

"Don't you know that I have come to eat you?" asked the dove.

15

"Oh, I know you won't eat me," said the grasshopper.

"Why not?" asked the dove.

"If a man was going to eat you, how would you feel?" asked the grasshopper.

"I should feel sad," answered the dove.

"Do you like to feel sad?" asked the grasshopper.

"No," answered the dove.

"If the man let you go, how would you feel?" asked the grasshopper.

"I should feel glad," answered the dove.

"Do you like to feel glad?" asked the grasshopper.

"Yes," answered the dove.

"I should feel sad if you were going to eat me," said the grasshopper. "I shall feel glad if you let me go. Do you want me to feel sad, or do you want me to feel glad?"

"I want you to feel glad," said the dove. "I will not eat you. I will let you go."

"I knew you would," said the grasshopper. "We must all be kind, for we are all friends and brothers." —INDIAN FABLE.

17

water   (weather)
pretty   feather
         (ought)
         thought
         enough
         swan
         use

WHY RAVENS CROAK

A raven was very unhappy because his feathers were black.

One day he saw a beautiful white swan swimming in a lake.

"How beautiful and white her feathers

18

are," he thought. "It must be because she washes them so much. Why, she almost lives in the water. If I should wash my feathers all day long, they might get white, too. I will try it."

So he flew from his nest in the woods, and lived for days near the lake.

Every day he washed his feathers from morning to night.

But his feathers did not get white.

They were just as black as ever.

But the raven was not used to living in water, so he caught a very bad cold.

At last he flew back to his nest in the wood.

"It is no use," he croaked. "I can never be white. I do not want to be white. Black feathers are pretty enough for me. Croak! Croak!"

All ravens have said "Croak! Croak!" ever since.

(pea)	(feed)	(rock)
speak	indeed	peacock

laughed	(full)	(not)
only	pulled	lot
steal	(cool)	among
	foolish	

THE PROUD CROW

One day a crow found a lot of peacock feathers.

"My," cried the silly crow, "how lucky I am. No other crow in the world will look as fine as I. How all my old friends will envy me!"

And the proud crow stuck the peacock feathers all over his back.

20

Then he flew away to show himself to his
friends.

He strutted up and down before them.

But they did not envy him.

They only laughed at him.

"Just look at that silly bird!" they cried.
"See him strut! Did you ever see anything
so proud? Caw, caw, caw!"

The proud crow was now very angry.

"Do not speak to me," he said. "I have

fine feathers. I am a peacock. I will have
nothing to do with you crows."

So off he strutted to the peacocks.

"How do you do, my dear friends?" he
said in his sweetest voice.

"Who are you?" cried the peacocks.

"Do you not see that I am a peacock?" answered the crow. "Look at my fine feathers."

"Fine feathers, indeed! We threw those old feathers away long ago. You are no peacock. You are just an old black crow."

Then the peacocks fell upon the old crow and pulled off all his fine feathers.

They tore out many of his own feathers, too.

The foolish crow was a sight!

He crept back to his old friends.

He tried to steal in among them without being seen.

But they all cried out, "Who are you? What do you want here?"

"Don't you see that I am your old friend?" croaked the crow. "I am going to live with you always."

"No, you are not," answered a wise old crow. "You are no friend of ours. A few old

peacock feathers made you think you were
a peacock. So you left your old friends. The
peacocks saw you were a cheat and drove you
away. Hereafter you must live alone. Be off
with you!"

And all the crows said, "Caw, caw, caw!
Caw, caw, caw!"

(hark)	(hive)	often
dark	lively	wolf

(much)	(leg)	owl
such	begged	growled
		howled

noise	(head)	
	dead	

THE WOLF AND THE KID

One day a little kid was lost in a dark wood.

He ran on and on, but could not find his way out.

At last he became frightened and began to bleat.

"Mother! Mother!" he called.

25

His mother did not hear him; but a hungry wolf did.

"Just what I want for my dinner!" he howled.

"Oh, Mr. Wolf!" cried the little kid, "please show me the way home."

"Show you the way home!" growled the wolf. "I am hungry and I'm going to eat you."

26

"Oh, please, please, Mr. Wolf," begged the frightened kid, "please let me go!"

"No, no, I'll eat you," growled the wolf.

And he sprang at the poor, frightened little kid.

"Oh, Mr. Wolf," bleated the kid, "I have heard that you make very fine music. I love to dance. Please sing for me, so that I may have one more dance before I die. It is not much to ask."

This pleased the wolf, for he was proud of his singing.

"Well," he growled, "music is good before eating. I often sing before my dinner. To-day I was too hungry to think of it. But I will sing just one song. Then I will eat you. Dance lively, now!"

So the wolf howled a song, and the kid danced his best.

When the wolf stopped, the kid cried, "That was good. But you did not sing loud enough or fast enough for me. Is that the best you can do?"

"No," said the wolf. "I can sing louder and faster than any one in the woods. Listen!"

So the wolf sang louder and faster, and the kid danced livelier and better than before.

But the wolf made so much noise that the dogs heard it. They came running into the woods to see what was the matter.

When the wolf saw the dogs, he stopped singing and ran for his life. The dogs rushed after him.

But the wise little kid trotted safely home to his mother.

"I have to go without my dinner," growled the wolf. "I alone am to blame. I should kill and eat kids, not sing for them."

(quick)   (deer)   (thank)   (east)

chick   queer   bank   least

chicken

splash   even   each   stream

sail

QUEER CHICKENS

An old hen found a nest behind the gate.
It was full of eggs. Such beautiful eggs!
They would make any old hen's heart glad.

"I will sit on these eggs. I will keep them warm," thought the hen. "Then a little chicken will come out of each one."

So the old hen spread her wings over the eggs. How very wide she had to spread them!

For many days she sat there waiting.

One morning she awoke to find her nest full of little ones.

"One, two, three, four, five, six, seven, eight, nine, ten, eleven, twelve," she counted.

"Cluck, cluck, what dear little chickens," said the hen.

"Come and get breakfast. Cluck, cluck, cluck, cluck! What hungry chickens!

Now I will let you play in the meadow. Come down to the brook first and get a drink.

The water is clear and cool. Do not go too near, or you will fall in."

Now, what do you think those little ones did?

You never could guess, so I will tell you.

As soon as they saw the brook they ran to it. They ran as fast as ever they could go.

They rushed right into the water.

"Cluck, cluck! Cluck, cluck! Come back! Come back!" called the old hen. "Come back, come back to your mother."

But they did not come back.

They did not even listen.

They sailed clear across the stream.

They sailed up stream and they sailed down stream.

But they did not come back to their mother.

She could only run up and down the bank, looking and calling.

"What shall I do? What shall I do?" she cried, "Come back! Come back, you naughty chickens. You will drown, every one of you, I know you will drown. O, why will you not mind your mother?"

How frightened she was!

She just knew all her dear chicks would drown.

Still she did not dare to follow them into the water. She never swam a stroke in all her life. She never even waded in the water.

But such fun as her little ones were having! They were not the least bit afraid.

They swam and splashed around all day.

All day the old mother hen ran up and

down the bank calling and begging, "Come back! Come back! Come right back to your mother!"

At last the little ones were tired.

Then they came back to their frightened mother.

One after another came up the bank and ran to her.

How glad she was to gather them again under her warm wings.

But what queer chickens they were.

(who)	believe	(caught)	roam
whose	sure	naughty	ma'am

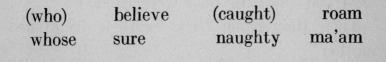

LITTLE DUCKS

"My dears, whatever are you at?
  You ought to be at home;
I told you not to wet your feet,
  I told you not to roam.

Oh, dear! I'm sure you will be drowned,
  I never saw such tricks;
Come home at once and go to bed,
  You naughty, naughty chicks!"

Now most of them were five days old,
  But one, whose age was six—
"Please, ma'am," said he, "I think
    we're ducks;
I don't believe we're chicks."

—ROBERT MACK.

ugly   (wise)
push   rise

THE CATERPILLAR

I creep upon the ground, and the children say,
"You ugly old thing!" and push me away.

I lie in my bed, and the children say,
"The fellow is dead, we'll throw him away."

At last I awake, and the children try
To make me stay, as I rise and fly.

(fellow)	(age)	(speak)	(ice)
bellow	cage	creak	mice
		squeak	climbed
(high)	(box)		uprooted
sighed	ox	roared	burrowed
bear	Tumtollo	breathes	

40

WHO IS STRONGEST?

Once upon a time Tumtollo climbed a tree.
The wind blew hard and uprooted the tree.
Tumtollo was thrown to the ground.

"Oh, oh, oh!" he cried with pain, "oh, oh, oh!"

"My, isn't the tree strong!" cried he; "it
can throw Tumtollo to the ground."

"You are wrong," creaked the tree. "I am
not strong. If I were, could I be uprooted
by the wind?"

"Ah, I see," said Tumtollo, "it is the wind
that is strong.

The wind uprooted the tree.

The tree threw Tumtollo to the ground."

"No, friend, you are wrong," sighed the
wind. "If I were strong, could I be stopped
by the hill?"

"Oh, I see now," said Tumtollo, "it is the
hill that is strong.

41

The hill stopped the wind.

The wind uprooted the tree.

The tree threw Tumtollo to the ground."

"Wrong again," said the hill. "I am not strong. If I were, I should not be burrowed by mice."

"Oh," said Tumtollo, "then it is the mouse that is strong.

The mouse burrowed the hill.

The hill stopped the wind.

The wind uprooted the tree.

The tree threw Tumtollo to the ground."

"Still wrong," squeaked the mouse. "It is

not I who am strong. If I were, could the cat catch me?"

"Well, then, it is the cat that is strong," said Tumtollo.

"The cat caught the mouse.
The mouse burrowed the hill.
The hill stopped the wind.
The wind uprooted the tree.
The tree threw Tumtollo to the ground."

"No, Tumtollo, I am not strong," mewed the cat. "If I were, could the dog frighten me?"

"Then it is the dog who is strong," said Tumtollo.

"The dog frightened the cat.

The cat caught the mouse.
The mouse burrowed the hill.
The hill stopped the wind.
The wind uprooted the tree.
The tree threw Tumtollo to the ground."

"It is not I who am strong," barked the dog.
"If I were, would the ox hook me with his horns?"

"Then it must be the ox who is strong," said Tumtollo.

"The ox hooked the dog.
The dog frightened the cat.
The cat caught the mouse.
The mouse burrowed the hill,
The hill stopped the wind.
The wind uprooted the tree.
The tree threw Tumtollo to the ground."

"No," bellowed the ox, "I am not strong. If I were, would the bee sting me?"

"Ah, ha! it is the little bee that is strong,"
said Tumtollo.

"The bee stung the ox.

The ox hooked the dog.

The dog frightened the cat.

The cat caught the mouse.

The mouse burrowed the hill.

The hill stopped the wind.

The wind uprooted the tree.

The tree threw Tumtollo to the ground."

"No, no!" buzzed the bee, "it is not I
who am strong. If I were would the bear
steal my honey?"

"Indeed, then, it is the bear who is strong,"
said Tumtollo.

"The bear robbed the bee.

The bee stung the ox.

The ox hooked the dog.

The dog frightened the cat.

The cat caught the mouse.

45

The mouse burrowed the hill.

The hill stopped the wind.

The wind uprooted the tree.

The tree threw Tumtollo to the ground."

"You are wrong, Tumtollo," growled the bear. "If I were strong, could the lion drive me away from my dinner?"

"Very well, then it is the lion who is strong," said Tumtollo.

"The lion drove away the bear.

The bear robbed the bee.

The bee stung the ox.

The ox hooked the dog.

The dog frightened the cat.

The cat caught the mouse.

The mouse burrowed the hill.

The hill stopped the wind.

The wind uprooted the tree.

The tree threw Tumtollo to the ground."

"It is not I who am strong," roared the lion. "If I were, could the rope bind me?"

"Just as you say," said Tumtollo, "then it is the rope that is strong.

The rope bound the lion.

The lion drove away the bear.

The bear robbed the bee.

The bee stung the ox.

The ox hooked the dog.

The dog frightened the cat.

The cat caught the mouse.

The mouse burrowed the hill.

The hill stopped the wind.

The wind uprooted the tree.

The tree threw Tumtollo to the ground."

"It is not I, indeed, that am strong," said the rope. "If I were could the fire burn me?"

"Well, well, then the fire must be strong," said Tumtollo.

"The fire burned the rope.
The rope bound the lion.
The lion drove away the bear.
The bear robbed the bee.
The bee stung the ox.
The ox hooked the dog.
The dog frightened the cat.
The cat caught the mouse.
The mouse burrowed the hill.
The hill stopped the wind.
The wind uprooted the tree.
The tree threw Tumtollo to the ground."

"No, no, Tumtollo," snapped the fire. "I am not strong. If I were, could the water put me out?"

"The water it is, then, that is strong," said Tumtollo.

"The water put out the fire.
The fire burned the rope.
The rope bound the lion.
The lion drove away the bear.
The bear robbed the bee.
The bee stung the ox.
The ox hooked the dog.
The dog frightened the cat.
The cat caught the mouse.
The mouse burrowed the hill.
The hill stopped the wind.
The wind uprooted the tree.
The tree threw Tumtollo to the ground."

"You are still wrong, Tumtollo," sang the water in a spring near by. "I am not strong. But I will tell you who is truly strong. It is Man.

Man drinks the water.
Man lights the fire.
Man makes the rope.
Man cages the lion.

Man tames the bear.

Man eats the bee's honey.

Man drives the ox.

Man keeps the dog.

Man feeds the cat.

Man kills the mouse.

Man digs the hill.

Man breathes the wind.

Man fells the tree.

Man rises when he is thrown to the ground."

Tumtollo said, "Yes, man is the strongest. Some day I shall be a man. Man rises when he is thrown to the ground. I will rise now."

So Tumtollo jumped up.

"Now I am the strongest," he said. "I have done what a man would do."

Then Tumtollo drank from the spring and ran home.

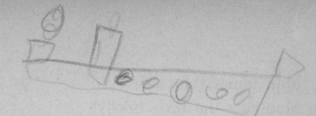

cave	everybody	coward
(other)		people
brother		(walk)
sunbeam	hollow	talk

THE DARK PLACE

A TEACHER–PUPIL STORY

Teacher

One morning a bear rushed from a cave into the bright sunshine. He was trembling and shaking with fear.

Pupils

"What is the matter, Brother Bear?" asked a wolf.

"O Brother Wolf!" said the bear, "I have just been in that cave. It is the darkest place in the world. It is so dark that I was frightened and ran out."

"Poof!" said the wolf, "I did not know you were such a coward, Brother Bear. I'm not afraid of the dark."

"Go in, then," said the bear.

"I will," said the wolf, and away he went into the cave. But he did not stay long. He soon came running out just as much frightened as the bear.

Teacher

When the bear saw the wolf, he stopped trembling and began to mock him.

Pupils

"Woof!" said the bear, "I did not know that you were such a coward, Brother Wolf. I thought you were not afraid of the dark."

"That's the darkest place in the world," said the wolf. "Everybody would be afraid there."

"Who! who would be afraid?" asked the owl. "Not I. I like dark places. I am little,

52

but I can go where the great bear and the great wolf are afraid to go. I will go into the dark cave and make my home there. I am not a coward like you."

So the owl flew into the cave. But he did not stay long. He soon came flying out just as much frightened as the bear and the wolf had been.

Teacher

When the bear and the wolf saw that the owl trembled with fear, they began to mock him.

Pupils

"Poof!" said the wolf. "So you are a coward, too, Brother Owl. I thought you liked dark places."

"I do," said the owl, "but not so dark as that cave. It is darker than my hollow tree is at night when the moon and all the stars are hidden. I almost lost my way."

53

"Woof!" said the bear. "I thought you were going to make your home there."

"Not I," said the owl. "It is too dark for me. Brother Wolf is right. It is the darkest place in the world. Nothing can stay there."

"Where is this darkest place?" asked a little sunbeam. "I have heard so many people talk about dark places and I have never seen one. Are you sure this is a dark place?"

"It is," said the owl.

"It's the darkest place in the world," said the bear.

"Go in and see," said the wolf.

"I will," said the sunbeam, and it glided into the dark cave.

After a long time it came out.

"I don't know what you are talking about, my friends," it said. "I can't find any dark place. Please come in and show it to me."

At first the bear, the wolf, and the owl were afraid to go. But after a while they went into the cave with the sunbeam. And what do you think? They couldn't find the dark place.

"Where is the dark place?" asked the sunbeam.

"It was right here," said the bear.

"Where can it be now?" said the wolf.

"I am so wise, I will find out," said the owl.

He hunted and hunted and hunted, and the sunbeam went with him, but he never found the dark spot for the sunbeam to see.

Can you tell why not?

(honey)	(this)	(rob)	(each)
money	miss	cob	peach
pieces	(carry)	lost	rooster
sharp	marry	buy	hurried

THE ANT AND THE MOUSE

There was once an ant.

While sweeping her house one day, this ant found three pieces of money.

"What shall I buy?" said she.

"Shall I buy fish?"

"No, fish is full of bones. I can't eat bones. I'll not buy fish."

"Shall I buy bread?"

"No, bread has crust. I can't eat crust. I'll not buy bread."

57

"Shall I buy peaches?"

"No, peaches have stones. I can't eat stones. I'll not buy peaches."

"Shall I buy corn?"

"No, corn grows on a cob. I can't eat cobs. I'll not buy corn."

"Shall I buy apples?"

"No, apples have seeds. I can't eat seeds. I'll not buy apples."

"Shall I buy a ribbon?"

"Yes, that's just what I want. I will buy a ribbon."

And away ran Miss Ant to the store and bought her a bright red ribbon.

She tied the ribbon about her neck and sat in her window.

An ox came along and said, "How pretty you are, Miss Ant! Will you marry me?"

"Sing," said the ant, "so I may hear your voice."

The ox was very proud of his voice and he bellowed with all his might.

"No, no," cried the ant, "I'll not marry you, Mr. Ox. Your bellow frightens me. Go away."

Soon a lion came that way and said, "How pretty you are, Miss Ant! Will you marry me?"

"Sing," said the ant, "so I may hear your voice."

The lion was proud of his voice and he roared with all his might.

"No, no," cried the ant, "I'll not marry you,

Mr. Lion. Your loud roar frightens me. It shakes the very hills. Go away."

The lion had not been gone long when a proud rooster came strutting along that way.

"How pretty you are, Miss Ant! Will you marry me?" said the rooster.

"Sing," said the ant, "so I may hear your voice."

The rooster was very proud of his shrill voice and he crowed with all his might.

"No, no," cried the ant, "I'll not marry you, Mr. Rooster. Your shrill crow frightens me. Go away."

The rooster was hardly out of sight when a big dog came trotting that way.

"How pretty you are, Miss Ant! Will you marry me?" said the dog.

"Sing," said the ant, "so I may hear your voice."

The dog was very proud of his voice and he barked with all his might.

"No, no," cried the ant, "I'll not marry you, Mr. Dog. Your sharp bark frightens me. Go away."

After a time a wee little mouse came frisking that way.

"How pretty you are, Miss Ant! Will you marry me?" said the mouse.

"Sing," said the ant, "so I may hear your voice.

Now the wee little mouse was not at all proud of his voice. But he squeaked as sweetly as he could, "Wee, wee, wee!"

"Yes, yes," cried the ant, "I'll marry you,

dear Mouse. Your sweet little voice pleases me. Come right in."

In scampered the mouse.

The ant gave him two pieces of money, for she had spent only one on her ribbon.

He hurried away to the store, and came quickly back bringing apples and bread.

Mrs. Ant Mouse now sat down to a feast.

Mr. Mouse ate the crusts and the seeds, so nothing was lost.

Songs of Life.

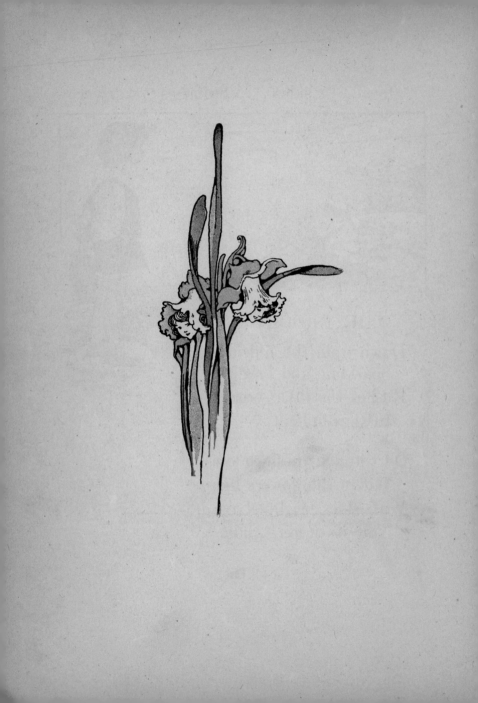

(flies) skies branches river

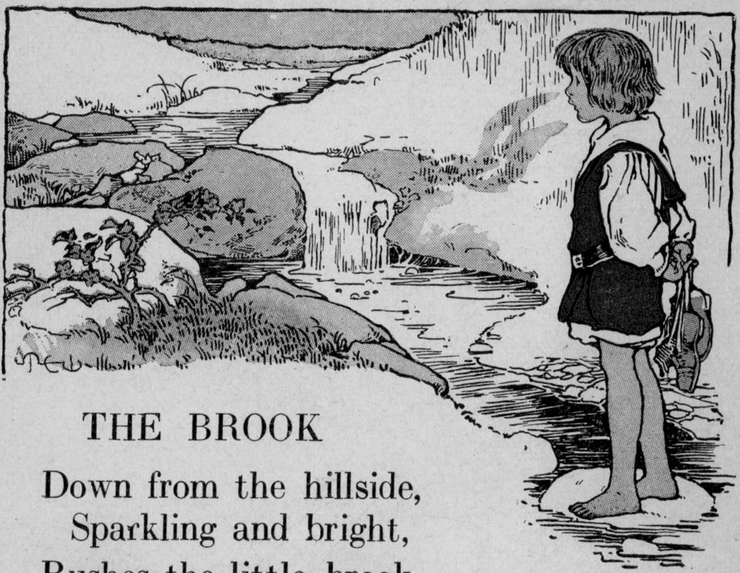

THE BROOK

Down from the hillside,
Sparkling and bright,
Rushes the little brook,
In the sunlight.

On through the meadow,
Where the flowers hide,
With skies bright above it,
Now its waters glide.

. . . . .

Tall trees beside the brook,
  Their branches o'er it throw,
As through the quiet woodland,
  The sparkling waters flow.

So it hurries down the hillside,
  And across the meadow sweet,
And through the shady woodland,
  Till the river it shall meet.

66

farm   (tip)   clothes   life
shoes   slip   hurt

A TRUE STORY

A TEACHER–PUPIL STORY

Teacher

Dick was a little boy who lived in a great
big city. He had never been in the country
in all his life. One summer he went with his
mother to visit his grandfather who lived on
a farm in the country.

Pupils

There was a little brook on the farm. One
morning Mother took Dick to see the brook.

"When I was a little girl," said Mother,
"I liked to wade in this brook."

"How did you wade in the brook?" asked Dick.
He had never seen anybody wading in the water.

67

"I took off my shoes and stockings and walked in the water," said Mother.

"Oh, Mother, please may I wade in the water?" begged Dick.

Mother laughed. "Indeed you may," she said. "I want you to."

So Dick took off his shoes and stockings and ran down to the brook. He put one foot into the water.

"Ouch!" he cried as he pulled his foot out. "The water is as cold as ice."

Mother laughed again. "After you have waded for a little while you won't mind the cold," she said.

Teacher

It took Dick some time to get used to the cold water, but after a while he liked it, and waded about, splashing the water and laughing aloud. Mother sat down under a shady tree and took out her sewing.

Pupils

"May I walk down the brook, Mother?" asked Dick.

"Yes. The water is not deep. But don't slip on the stones or you will fall and get your clothes wet," said Mother.

"No, Mother, I won't slip," answered Dick, and waded off.

How still it was! Soon Dick tried to see how quietly he could walk. He lifted his feet so carefully, and put them into the water without making a sound.

He saw an old log lying in the brook. "I will wade out to the log," he thought.

He waded out to the log, going oh, so softly.
"I will step up on the log and look around,"
he thought.

Just as he was about to put his foot on the
log, he saw — What do you think? —

Three big green frogs sitting on the log!

Now, Dick had never seen a frog before.
He was afraid they would hurt him.

Down went his foot into the water with a
loud splash.

The splash frightened the frogs. They jumped from the log into the water. Dick thought they were coming after him. He was afraid that they would bite his bare toes.

"Mother! Mother!" he cried, and turned to run away. But he slipped on the stones. Down he fell right into the brook.

Mother heard him call and came running along the bank to see what was the matter. She soon saw Dick lying in the water and splashing around.

"Jump up, Dick," she called. "My, how wet you are!"

Dick jumped up and ran to his mother. He told her all about the big "green things" that had frightened him.

Mother laughed and said, "How about the poor frogs? Don't you think that they were afraid of a big boy like you? What do you think they are telling their mother right now?"

"Why, mother, I wouldn't hurt them,' said Dick. "They need not be afraid of me."

"No, and they would not hurt you," said Mother. "You need not be afraid of them. But come home now and get into some dry clothes."

Teacher

Before the summer was over, Dick lost his fear of the frogs. He would have liked to play with them, but they always dived when he came too near.

72

Often Dick would ask them, "What did you tell your mother when you went home that first day I saw you?" But the frogs only blinked their eyes and said nothing.

Now what do you suppose they really did tell their mother about Dick?

CALLING THE VIOLET

Dear little Violet,
  Don't be afraid!
Lift your blue eyes
  From the rock's mossy shade.
All the birds call for you
  Out of the sky;
May is here waiting,
  And here, too, am I.

Come, pretty Violet,
  Winter's away;
Come, for without you
  May isn't May.
Down through the sunshine
  Wings flutter and fly;
Quick, little Violet,
  Open your eye!

—Lucy Larcom.

74

neither

trembling

THE WIND

Who has seen the wind?
  Neither I nor you;
But when the leaves hang trembling,
  The Wind is passing through.

Who has seen the wind?
  Neither you nor I;
But when the trees bow down their heads,
  The Wind is passing by.

different   ladies

young   skirts

THE WIND

I saw you toss the kites on high
And blow the birds about the sky;
And all around I heard you pass,
Like ladies' skirts across the grass—
   O wind, a-blowing all day long,
   O wind, that sings so loud a song!

I saw the different things you did,
But always you yourself you hid.

I felt you push, I heard you call,
I could not see yourself at all—
  O wind, a-blowing all day long,
  O wind, that sings so loud a song!

O you that are so strong and cold,
O blower, are you young or old?
Are you a beast of field and tree,
Or just a stronger child than me?
  O wind, a-blowing all day long,
  O wind, that sings so loud a song!

—R. L. Stevenson.

THE WIND'S SURPRISE

One day in spring the wind was blowing about. He saw a boy trying to fly a kite.

The boy would run and the kite would go up a little way. Then the boy would stop running and the kite would fall to the ground.

"What a lazy kite," said the wind. "I will make it fly."

He flew down to the kite.

"Ooo—Ooo—Ooo," he blew. "Why don't you fly up, you lazy kite? Get up! get up! get up!"

He blew and blew and the kite rose high in the air.

The boy laughed and called, "Thank you, good wind, for making my kite fly."

"He is a nice boy," said the wind. "I am glad I made his kite fly. I like to play with

78

boys." After a while the boy went home.
Then the wind flew off and soon he saw
another boy. This boy was walking along
very slowly.

"There is another boy," said the wind.
"He does not look happy. I will play with
him."

Down rushed the wind. The boy had no

kite to fly. So the wind blew his cap off and flew away with it.

"Oh!" cried the boy. "How I hate the wind!"

The wind was so surprised he dropped the cap to the ground.

The boy picked up his cap, put it on his head and ran home.

"Well!" said the wind. "I am surprised. One boy liked to have me play with him, and the other boy didn't. How can I tell what to do? Boys are queer!"

father   rolling   western   breathe

SWEET AND LOW

Sweet and low, sweet and low,
Wind of the western sea!
Low, low, breathe and blow,
Wind of the western sea,
Over the rolling waters go,
Come from the dying moon and blow,
Blow him again to me;
While my little one, while my pretty one, sleeps.

Sleep and rest, sleep and rest,
Father will come to thee soon;
Rest, rest, on mother's breast,
Father will come to thee soon;
Father will come to his babe in the nest,
Silver sails all out of the west,
Under the silver moon;
Sleep, my little one, sleep, my pretty one, sleep.

—TENNYSON.

81

folks (sure) oddest (out) born (seen)
jolly pure   shout guides queen

BABY–LAND

Boy

How many miles to Baby-land?

Girl

Anyone can tell;
Up one flight,

To the right,
Please to ring the bell.

Girl

What can you see in Baby-land?

Boy

Little folks in white—
  Downy heads,
  Cradle-beds,
Faces pure and bright.

Boy

What do they do in Baby-land?

Girl

Dream and wake and play,
  Laugh and crow,
  Shout and grow;
Jolly times have they!

Girl

What do they say in Baby-land?

Boy

Why, the oddest things;
    Might as well
    Try to tell
What the birdie sings!

Girl

Who is the Queen of Baby-land?

Boy

Mother, kind and sweet;
    And her love,
    Born above,
Guides the little feet.

—George Cooper.

(dress)
guess
shepherdess

SLEEP, BABY, SLEEP!

Sleep, baby, sleep!
Thy father watches his sheep;
Thy mother is shaking the dreamland tree,
And down comes a little dream on thee.
Sleep, baby, sleep!

Sleep, baby, sleep!
The large stars are the sheep;
The little stars are the lambs, I guess
The gentle moon is the shepherdess.
Sleep, baby, sleep!

earth   close   middle

HOW WE GOT OUR FIRST DAISIES

Long, long ago there were no flowers on the earth. There was not even a daisy. The only thing that grew close to the ground was the green grass.

In those old days the sky was full of stars at night just as it is now. The little children that lived on the earth loved the stars.

One night some children were looking up at the sky.

"How bright the stars are," they said. "How we love them!"

"I would like to see one close," said a child. "I wonder what it is made of."

"I wonder, too," said another child.

Then all the children looked up at the brightest star and sang,

"Twinkle, twinkle, little star,
How I wonder what you are."

"I wish we had some stars on the earth," said another child.

Now while the children were talking, dear Lady Moon heard them.

"They shall have some of my stars," she said. "I will send some to them tonight."

She waited until all the children were fast asleep. Then she called her little stars to her.

"Dear star children," she said, "the little

earth children love you. They want some of you to go and live on the earth. Who will go and make the children happy?"

"I will!" "I will!" "I will!" cried some of the stars.

"Thank you, little stars," she said. "You must go now while the children are asleep. In the morning they will find you growing in the grass."

Lady Moon kissed each little star as it dropped to the earth.

These stars became our first daisies. In the middle of each daisy you will find something round and yellow like the moon. That is where Lady Moon kissed the little star when it left its home in Skyland.

roving   pale

LADY MOON

Child. Lady Moon, Lady Moon, where are
you roving?

Moon. Over the sea.

Child. Lady Moon, Lady Moon, whom are
you loving?

Moon. All that love me.

Child. Are you not tired with rolling, and never
Resting to sleep?
Why look so pale and so sad, as forever
Wishing to weep?

Moon. Ask me not this, little child, if you
love me;
You are too bold;
I must obey my dear Father above me.
And do as I'm told.

Child. Lady Moon, Lady Moon, where are
   you roving?

Moon. Over the sea.

Child. Lady Moon, Lady Moon, whom are
   you loving?

Moon. All that love me.

—LORD HOUGHTON.

With Nature's Children

(lazy)	(bear)	(gather)
crazy	wearing	rather
swallows	(cave)	perhaps
together	save	honest
pleasant	bravely	passion
duller	June	color

DISCONTENT

Down in the field, one day in June,
  The flowers all bloomed together,
Save one, who tried to hide herself,
  And drooped—that pleasant weather.

A robin, who had flown too high
  And felt a little lazy,
Was resting near a buttercup,
  Who wished she were a daisy.

For daisies grow so trim and tall;
   She always had a passion
For wearing frills around her neck,
   In just the daisies' fashion.

And buttercups must always be
   The same old, tiresome color,
While daisies dress in gold and white,
   Although their gold is duller.

"Dear robin," said this sad young flower,
   "Perhaps you'd not mind trying
To find a nice white frill for me
   Some day, when you are flying."

"You silly thing," the robin said,
   "I think you must be crazy;
I'd rather be my honest self
   Than any made-up daisy.

You're nicer in your own bright gown;
  The little children love you;
Be the best buttercup you can,
  And think no flower above you.

Though swallows leave me out of sight,
  We'd better keep our places.
Perhaps the world would go all wrong,
  With one too many daisies.

Look bravely up into the sky,
  And be content with knowing
That God wished for a buttercup
  Just here, where you are growing."

—SARAH ORNE JEWETT.

(snug)		(steal)
dug	pounce	meal
(awoke)	hole	(good)
spoke	stole	stood
family	warning	straight

BELLING THE CAT

A family of rats had their home in a barn. They made many snug nests in the warm hay. They dug holes through the hay from nest to nest.

They ran in and out and all about the barn. They had nothing to fear. When they were hungry they could always find grain in the stalls. They became very fat. And they were as happy a family of rats as one could wish to see.

But one day a big black cat found the rats' barn. That was a sad day for the rat family! This cat was not fat and he was not happy.

He was very thin, very cross, and very hungry.

He liked to eat rats. He liked to eat them better than anything else in the world.

How he did love nice, fat, happy rats! At last he had found them, a whole big family of them!

This hungry, greedy cat now ate rats for breakfast, rats for dinner, and rats for supper. And sometimes he had a rat between meals.

Very soon this cat began to grow fat and happy.

But happy cats make unhappy rats. While this cat grew fat, these rats grew thin.

Yet in the stalls there was just as much grain as ever. But the rats were afraid to go for it. They were afraid to leave their holes, for no rat could tell when the cat might pounce upon him.

That sly cat stole about without a sound.

The rats never heard him until he was close to them.

Then, pounce! The wicked cat's claws held a rat.

So, many a poor rat went to the stall, and never came back. And the rat family was growing smaller day by day.

At last the wise old rats saw that something must be done. So they called a meeting of all the rats that were still alive.

When all had come together in a safe place the oldest and wisest rat rose up on his hind legs.

He stood up very straight, very tall, and very thin.

"My dear brothers and sisters, my dear children and grandchildren!" began the wise old rat.

"You all know the one fear of our lives."

"The cat!" whispered the little rats.

"Yes, the cat," said the old rat. "He has grown fat and sleek feeding on your brothers, your mothers, your wives, and your children.

He may eat me today, or you, or you, or you. Who can tell?

He steals upon us without warning.

He is never seen, he is never heard, until it is too late.

I have called you together to see what can be done to stop him.

Who has a plan?"

The old rat waited.

All the other rats looked from one to another, but no one spoke.

"Well, then," said the wise old rat at last, "listen to me.

If we only knew where the cat was, we could not be caught. If we could only hear him coming, we might hide from him.

Now, my plan is this. We will hang a bell to that cat's neck."

"The very thing! Hurrah! Hurrah!" cried all the rats together.

"Why haven't we thought of that before?

No more of us will go to make dinners for that old cat.

Now, we will have all the corn we can eat! Come on!"

And away sprang the hungry rats for the stalls.

"Stop! Stop!" cried the wise old rat. "Come back to your places!

The bell isn't on the cat's neck yet."

Slowly and sadly the hungry rats came back.

"Now," said the old rat, "who will tie the bell around the cat's neck?"

"Not I! Not I! Not I!" squeaked the poor frightened rats.

Then they sat very still and looked at each other.

Oh, how hungry they were! But not one dared to hang the bell on the cat's neck.

One by one they began to steal away.

Do you think they were going to look for the cat?

No, they were stealing softly to their holes.

Rat families still live in barns. Cats still feed upon them for no rat has ever tied a bell to a cat's neck.

102

THREE OF US KNOW

Who are my playfellows?
  Wait, you shall see;
Sometimes a little bird,
  Sometimes a bee.
All through the summer world
  Gayly we go.
Where is the greenest close,
Where is the sweetest rose,
  Three of us know.

Bee seeks the rose's heart,
  Bird seeks the tree,
I seek a little brook
  Clear as can be.

It singeth all day long
  Sweetly and low,
Ballad of sun and star;
What its song secrets are
  Three of us know.

Bee takes the honey home
  To the Queen bee;
Bird seeks a nest that hides
  High in the tree;
I seek a little house
  Where sweet vines grow.
What in God's world is best —
Trees, flowers, home, and rest —
  Three of us know.

—MARIE VAN VORST.

105

gypsy

gild

idle

THE DANDELION

Little gypsy dandelion,
  Dancing in the sun,
Have you any curls to sell?
  "Not a single one!"

Little idle dandelion
  Then I'll mow you down.
What is it your good for, pray,
  With your golden crown?

"Ah! I gild the fields so green
  In the pleasant spring,
Shining like the morning star
  With the light I bring."

106

hooted   (home)   oriole   roofs
eagle   dome   trouble   build
(enough)   (leaves)   mountain   (afraid)
rough   eaves   (bud)   paid
valley   weave   mud   bottom
lesson   since

THE MAGPIE'S LESSON

Years and years ago—ever so many years ago—only one bird in the whole world knew how to build a nest. That wise bird was the magpie.

One day all the other birds came to the magpie. They wanted to learn how to build nests. They begged the magpie to teach them.

"Indeed, I am glad to teach you," said Mrs. Magpie. "Just listen and watch me. First, you must choose a tall tree, like this great oak. Then take sticks—"

"A tree," broke in the bold eagle, "a tree here in this valley! No trees nor valleys for me! My nest shall be on the highest cliff of the mountain."

And away flew the eagle without waiting
to hear more of the magpie's lesson. To this
day he puts together a few rough sticks on
a rocky, mountain cliff, and calls them a nest.

The magpie began again. "Take sticks like
these to a high branch," she said.

"Don't you know that the first strong wind
will blow your nest to the ground?" cried the
lark. "And the first boy who comes this way
will throw stones at it," put in Mrs. Bob-o-link.

"No high branches for us," sang the lark
and the bob-o-link together. And down they

flew into the tall grass of the meadow. They have made their nests there ever since.

Mrs. Magpie didn't even look at the birds flying away. "Weave the sticks together in and out, so," said she cheerfully. "That will make the bottom of the nest."

"I'll not set my nest on a branch like that," spoke up the oriole. "The wind would surely blow it off, as the lark just said."

And the oriole flew away and hung her nest from little twigs. You may see it there today swinging in the wind, far out at the end of a long branch.

"Cover the inside of your nest with mud," Mrs. Magpie went on again. "Then line it with soft grass."

"Dear, dear, so much work to make a nest!' yawned the whip-poor-will. "I'm not going to take the trouble." And that lazy bird hasn't made a nest from that day to this.

110

She just lays her eggs in a hollow on the ground, or perhaps on a log.

"Who, who, who would go to all that trouble!" hooted the owl. "I think I have a better plan.'

She looked very wise, but said no more. You can guess what her plan was when you find her eggs in a crow's or a hawk's old nest.

"Now take more mud and sticks," began the magpie once more. "You should build a dome over your nest. That is to hide the little ones and to keep out the rain."

"Oh, never mind the dome," said the robin. "I will cover my little ones with my wings, I can hide them and keep off the rain."

"You are right, Mrs. Robin," said the crow. "We have no use for domes." And to this day neither robins nor crows have built domes over their nests.

Mrs. Magpie went on building her nest, just as she knew it ought to be built. Soon it was done, dome and all.

"Indeed, Mrs. Magpie," said the swallows, "we like your nest. The dome is a fine thing, but why should we build it? There are plenty of domes already built; we need only to make our nests under them."

Ever since then some swallows have made their nests under banks. Others have made theirs under roofs of open barns; and still others under eaves.

So all the birds flew away and left Mrs.

Magpie without saying "thank you." Each
one built her nest as she pleased. And each
one thought her way so much better than the
magpie's.

But the magpie still builds her nest in the
top of a high tree. She makes it of mud and
sticks and covers it with a dome.

crocus   merry   daffodils

THE BLUEBIRD

I know the song that the bluebird is singing —
Out in the apple tree where he is swinging.
Brave little fellow! the skies may be dreary;
Nothing cares he while his heart is so cheery.

Hark! how the music leaps out from his throat.
Hark! was there ever so merry a note?
Listen a while and you'll hear what he's saying
Up in the apple tree swinging and swaying:

"Dear little blossoms down under the snow,
You must be weary of winter, I know
Hark! while I sing you a message of cheer:
Summer is coming, and springtime is here.

Little white snowdrops! I pray you arise;
Bright yellow crocus! come, open your eyes;
Daffodils! Daffodils! say, do you hear?
Summer is coming, and springtime is here!"

—Mrs. Emily Huntington Miller.

THE WOLF AND THE STORK

A greedy wolf got a bone stuck in his throat. Try as he would he could not get the bone out. At last he lay down to die, as he thought. But just then a stork came that way.

"Good day, Mr. Wolf," said the stork, kindly.

But the wolf could not answer a word.

The stork soon saw what the matter was, and with his long beak pulled the bone out of the wolf's throat. Without a word, the greedy wolf sprang up and went on with his dinner.

The stork, who was very hungry, began to pick up a few morsels of meat.

"Be off with you!" snapped the wolf. "How dare you touch my meat!"

"Is that the thanks I get for saving your life?" said the stork.

"Thanks!" answered the wolf, "did I not let you draw your bill out of my jaws in safety? It is you who should be thankful."

117

roebuck   Manitou   breezes

papoose   slumbering   prairie

THE INDIAN MOTHER'S LULLABY

Rock-a-by, hush-a-by, little papoose,
  The stars come into the sky;
The whip-po'-will's crying, the daylight is dying,
  The river runs murmuring by.

The pine trees are slumbering, little papoose,
  The squirrel has gone to his nest;
The robins are sleeping, the mother bird's
    keeping
The little ones warm with her breast.

The roebuck is dreaming, my little papoose,
  His mate lies asleep at his side;

118

The breezes are pining, the moonbeams are
    shining
    All over the prairies wide.

Then hush-a-by, rock-a-by, little papoose,
    You sail on the river of dreams;
Dear Manitou loves you, and watches above
    you,
    Till time when the morning light gleams.

—CHARLES MYALL.

119

stranger   won   foot
farther   shoot   mouth

THE BOASTER AND THE BABY
A TEACHER–PUPIL STORY
Teacher

One day some Indians were resting near their wigwams when a stranger joined them.

At once he began to boast of the great things he could do.

Pupils

"I can run faster than any man here," he said.

"Race with him, Light-foot," cried the Indians.

The Indian called Light-foot raced with the stranger.

Light-foot ran very fast, but the stranger ran faster and soon passed Light-foot and won the race.

"Does any other man want to race with me?" asked the stranger.

"No," answered the other Indians. "Light-foot is our fastest runner. If you can beat him, you can beat any of us."

Then the stranger said proudly, "I can not only beat in running, I can jump farther than any man here. Who will jump with me?"

"I will jump with you," said the best Indian jumper.

The Indian jumped first. You should have seen how far he jumped. "Good! good!" cried the other Indians. "That is a long jump. Can you jump as far as that, stranger?"

"I can jump farther," answered the stranger.

He jumped, and his jump was three times as long as the Indian's jump.

Then the stranger said, "I can shoot farther than any of you. I can kill more deer than any of **you**. I can walk longer. I can fight longer. There is nothing that I cannot do better than any of you."

Teacher

Now the other Indians did not like to hear the stranger boast in this way. They wished with all their hearts that somebody in their tribe could do something that the stranger

could not do. But what? At last a squaw
who stood near spoke.

Pupils

"I have a little papoose at home that can
do something that you cannot do, stranger,"
she said.

"What!" cried the stranger. "A papoose
can do something that I cannot do! Show
me this wonderful baby."

"Come with me," said the mother.

She led him to her home. The other Indians
went too.

Teacher

There on a bear skin, on the floor of the
wigwam, lay a tiny papoose. He was curled
up *with his toe in his mouth.*

Pupils

"Look at him," said the mother. "Can you
do that?"

How all the Indians laughed!

But the stranger did not laugh. He looked at the baby for a long time. Then he lay down beside it. He tried to lie just like the baby. Next he took hold of his foot and tried to pull it into his mouth.

He pulled and pulled and pulled, but he could not get his toes near his mouth.

The Indians laughed and laughed.

"Here is somebody that you cannot beat," they cried.

"I can! I can! I will! I will!" cried the stranger. And he tried and tried and tried, but he could not get his toe into his mouth.

At last he jumped up and ran away.

"Don't run so fast," cried the Indians. "You are not in a race now. The papoose is not trying to catch you."

But the stranger ran faster and faster until he was out of sight.

"There," said the proud mother. "I knew my own little papoose could beat him."

After that whenever an Indian began to boast, somebody would say to him, "Don't boast. Everybody can be beaten at something. Remember how the boaster was beaten by a baby."

THE MOON

Moon, so round and yellow,
  Looking from on high,
How I love to see you
  Shining in the sky.
Oft and oft I wonder,
  When I see you there,
How they get to light you,
  Hanging in the air;

Where you go at morning,
  When the night is past,
And the sun comes peeping
  O'er the hills at last.
Sometime I will watch you
  Slyly overhead,
When you think I'm sleeping
  Snugly in my bed.

— MATTHIAS BARR.

In Story Land

pond	(push)	(hard)
	bush	yard
question	(ever)	earth
suddenly	clever	worm
chirped	silently	

HOW MRS. WHITE HEN HELPED ROSE

A beautiful rose tree grew in the garden. Every morning she smiled up at the golden sun. But one morning when the sun rose, he was surprised to see that his friend, the rose, drooped sadly. What could be the matter with her! He sent one of his warm rays down to earth to find out.

"Dear Rose," said the bright sunbeam, "why do you droop and look so sad?"

129

"Ah, me!" sighed the rose, "I am so unhappy! An ugly worm is eating my leaves, and he will not crawl away."

The sun felt very sorry for the rose. "I will not shine," he said, "until Rose is happy." So he hid behind a dark cloud.

The wind came hurrying along. "Father Sun," he cried, "why are you not shining today?"

"Ah, me!" answered the sun, "dear Rose is so unhappy! An ugly worm is eating her leaves, and he will not crawl away. I will shine no more until Rose is happy."

130

"I, too, am so sorry," whispered the wind. "I will blow no more until Rose is happy." So saying he dropped to the earth and was still.

A bird was surprised when the wind stopped.

"Mr. Wind," he called, "why have you stopped blowing?"

"Ah, me!" sighed the wind. "Dear Rose is so unhappy! An ugly worm is eating her leaves, and he will not crawl away. So Sun will shine no more and I will blow no more until Rose is happy."

"I, also, love Rose," sang the bird; "and I will sing no more until Rose is happy." He flew away silently to his nest in the oak tree.

"It is not night," said the old tree; "why are you not flying and singing, little bird?"

"Ah, me!" chirped the bird. "Dear Rose is so unhappy! An ugly worm is eating her leaves, and he will not crawl away. So Sun will shine no more, Wind will blow no more.

and I will sing no more until Rose is happy."

"That is all very sad," whispered the tree. "I shall drop no more acorns until Rose is happy."

Soon the squirrel came to gather some nuts. But he could find very few.

"Dear Tree," he chattered, "please drop down some acorns."

"No," answered the tree. "I cannot, now."

"Why not?" asked the squirrel.

"Ah, me!" rustled the tree. "Dear Rose is so unhappy! An ugly worm is eating her leaves, and he will not crawl away. So Sun will shine no more, Wind will blow no more, Bird will sing no more, and I will drop no more acorns until Rose is happy again."

"And I will work no more," chirped the squirrel. "I will run away to my nest in the old hollow tree."

On the way to his home the squirrel met Mrs. Brown Duck.

"Good morning, Mr. Squirrel," quacked the duck. "Why are you not working this morning?"

"Ah, me!" replied the squirrel. "Dear Rose is so unhappy! An ugly worm is eating her leaves, and he will not crawl away. So Sun will shine no more, Wind will blow no more, Bird will sing no more, Oak Tree will drop no more acorns, and I will work no more till Rose is happy."

"Then I will swim no more," said Mrs.

Brown Duck. And she waddled off to the barnyard. There she met Mrs. White Hen.

"Why do you look so sad, Mrs. Duck?" said the hen.

"Ah, me!" quacked the duck. "Dear Rose is so unhappy! An ugly worm is eating her leaves, and he will not crawl away. So Sun will shine no more, Wind will blow no more, Bird will sing no more, Oak Tree will drop no more acorns, Squirrel will work no more, and I will swim no more until Rose is happy again."

"Indeed! Indeed!" cackled Mrs. White Hen.

"Pray tell me how stopping your work will help Rose. If you wish Rose to be happy, you must do something for her. Come with me."

Away hurried the hen and the duck until they came to the rose. The old hen asked no questions. She did not even take time to say "Good morning." But she cocked her head first on one side, then on the other, searching through the leaves of the rosebush with her bright little eyes. Suddenly she darted forward. "Snap!" went her bill, and the worm was swallowed.

"There, Mrs. Duck," clucked the hen, "see how I have helped Rose and at the same time got a nice breakfast for myself."

At once the rose looked up toward the sun and smiled. Thereupon the sun began to shine.

"If I had only thought," said the sun, "I might have burned that worm with my hot rays."

"And I might have blown him away," whistled the wind, springing up suddenly.

"If I had only thought," sang the bird, "I might have had a nice fat worm for breakfast."

"And so might I," quacked the duck as she waddled away toward the pond.

The oak tree shook down a great shower of acorns, and the squirrel hastened to gather them. They, too, wished they had thought of some way to help Rose.

But the clever old white hen said nothing at all.

THE SANDMAN

The Sandman comes across the land,
  At evening, when the sun is low:
Upon his back a bag of sand—
  His step is soft and slow.
I never hear his gentle tread,
But when I bend my sleepy head,
"The Sandman's coming!" mother says,
And mother tells the truth, always!

I guess he's old, with silver hair,
  He's up so late! He has to go
To lots of children, everywhere,
  At evening, when the sun is low.
His cloak is long, and green and old,
With pretty dreams in every fold—
His shoes are silken, mother says,
And mother tells the truth, always!

He glides across the sunset hill,
  To seek each little child, like me:
Our all-day-tired eyes to fill
  With sands of sleep, from slumber's sea.
I try my best awake to stay,
But I am tired out with play;
"I'll never see him!" mother says,
And mother tells the truth—always!

— Marie Van Vorst.

139

(learn)
earn
shoulder
dollars
(give)
living
remember

daughter
melt
minute
pocket
donkey
hundred

LAZY JACK

A TEACHER–PUPIL STORY

Teacher

Once upon a time there was a poor widow who had an only son, named Jack. Jack was the laziest boy in the whole round world. He was too lazy even to join in the games that the other children played. His mother determined to cure him of his laziness; so one morning she called him before the sun was up.

Pupils

MOTHER: Get up, Jack! Get up, I say.

JACK: O Mother, let me rest. I am so tired.

MOTHER: Tired! You are lazy, I say. Everybody calls you "Lazy Jack," and they are right. You never do a bit of work. You sit in the sun in the summer; and you sit by the fire in the winter. You are too lazy even to play. Get up, I say.

JACK: Just let me sleep a little longer, Mother.

MOTHER: No, I won't let you sleep a minute longer. You are a big, strong boy. You must go out and work and earn your living.

JACK: Where can I go, Mother? What can I do?

141

MOTHER: Go to Farmer Green. He says he
will take you to help him. He will
tell you what to do. Get up and
eat your breakfast, and start at
once.

JACK: Well, if I must, I will.

Teacher

All day the mother wondered how Jack was
behaving. When he came home in the even-
ening, she was waiting for him at the gate.

Pupils

MOTHER: Well, Jack, what did the farmer give
you for working today?

JACK: A penny, Mother.

MOTHER: Well, it is not much, but it will help
buy bread. Give it to me.

JACK: I lost the penny.

MOTHER: Lost it! How?

JACK: I put it in my mouth. When I

came to the brook, I stopped to get a drink, and the penny fell into the water.

MOTHER: You should have put the penny in your pocket and run home.

JACK: I will next time.

Teacher

The next day when Jack came home his mother saw that his coat was splashed with something white.

Pupils

MOTHER: What have you spilled all over your coat, Jack?

JACK: Milk, Mother. Farmer Green gave me a jug of milk for my day's work. I remembered what you told me last night so I put the jug in my pocket and ran home. The milk spilled all over me.

MOTHER: You foolish boy! You should have
carried the jug in your hand and
walked home slowly.

JACK: I will next time, Mother.

Teacher

Next day when Jack returned from work,
he held his hands behind his back. His
mother wondered what he was hiding. She
thought it must be something very nice.

MOTHER: What did the farmer give you for
working today?

JACK: Some butter, Mother.

MOTHER: Good! We will have some for our
supper. Where is it?

JACK: Here on my hands. I remembered what you told me last night; so I carried the butter in my hands and walked very slowly. The butter melted. Just see it on my hands!

MOTHER: You foolish, foolish boy! You should have cooled the butter in the brook, put it in some green leaves, and carried it home.

JACK: I will the next time.

Teacher

The fourth night Jack came home with empty hands.

Pupils

MOTHER: Well, Jack, what did you get for working today?

JACK: A cat, Mother.

MOTHER: Just what I wanted to kill the mice! Where is it?

JACK: I don't know, Mother. I remembered what you said last night; so I carried the cat down to the brook and tried to cool it in the water. But the cat didn't like the water. It scratched me, and jumped out of my arms and ran away. Just see how it scratched my face and hands!

MOTHER: You foolish, foolish boy! You should have tied a string around its neck, put it on the ground, and pulled it along.

JACK: I will next time.

146

Teacher

The fifth night Jack returned dragging a dirty looking bundle through the mud.

Pupils

MOTHER: What did the farmer give you to-day, Jack?

JACK: A loaf of bread, Mother.

MOTHER: That a loaf of bread! It looks like a roll of mud. How did it get so black?

JACK: I remembered what you told me last night; so I tied a string around it, put it on the ground, and pulled it along. That's how it got so black.

MOTHER: You foolish, foolish boy! You should have carried it home on your shoulder.

JACK: I will next time.

Next day the farmer gave Jack a donkey. Jack remembered what his mother had said;

so he got the donkey up on his shoulder and
walked away.

On the way home, he had to pass the home
of a very rich man. Now, the rich man had
a daughter who was very sad. She never,
never laughed. The rich man had said that
he would give a hundred dollars to anyone
who would make his daughter laugh.

The rich man and his daughter were sitting
at a window, when Jack came along carrying
the donkey on his shoulder. When the

daughter saw Jack and his donkey, she laughed and laughed and laughed. She had never seen anything so funny.

The rich man was so pleased that he gave Jack the hundred dollars at once. Jack put the money in his pocket, climbed upon the donkey's back and rode home.

When his mother saw the donkey and the hundred dollars, she said, "At last you know how to carry things home the right way."

polite   shoemaker   washerwoman

gentleman   crumbs   poor

A GOOD THANKSGIVING

Once upon a time there was an old man named Mr. Gay. Mr. Gay was always kind and polite, so everybody called him Gentleman Gay. He liked to help everybody and make them happy.

One Thanksgiving Day old Gentleman Gay said, "I'm going to have a good time today."

"How are you going to have a good time?" asked his wife.

Said Old Gentleman Gay,
"On Thanksgiving Day,
If you want a good time,
Give something away."

150

"Then give something to Shoemaker Price,"
said Mrs. Gay. "He is very poor and he has
ever so many children to feed."

"I will," said old Gentleman Gay. "I will
send him the biggest, fattest turkey I can find."

So old Gentleman Gay sent Shoemaker
Price a big fat turkey.

"Now I feel happy," said Gentleman Gay.
"I know I shall have a good time today."

Poor shoemaker Price had bought a chicken
for his Thanksgiving dinner. But the chicken

151

was very small and his family was very large. The chicken was so small, that each child could have only a tiny taste. When the children saw the big, fat turkey, they clapped their hands. "Good! good!" they cried. "Now we can have a good time!"

"Yes, but we must give somebody else a good time," said Shoemaker Price. "Let us send our little chicken to poor old Widow Lee."

One of Shoemaker Price's boys ran over to Widow Lee's house with the little chicken. When she saw it she was very glad. It was big enough for her.

"Thank you," she said. "Why did your father send this nice little chicken to me?"

"Old Gentleman Gay sent us a big fat turkey, and we are going to have a good time. We want you to have a good time too," said the boy. "That is why Father sent you the chicken."

"Then," said old Widow Lee, "I must make somebody else happy. I made a big pumpkin pie this morning. Now that I have this nice little chicken for my Thanksgiving dinner, I don't need the pie. I will take it to Washerwoman Winnie. It will taste good to her."

She took the big pumpkin pie to Washerwoman Winnie.

"Thank you," said the poor washerwoman, "but why did you bring your big pumpkin pie to me?"

"Shoemaker Price sent me a nice little chicken, and I am going to have that for my dinner. I want you to have a good dinner

too," said Widow Lee. "That is why I have given you my big pumpkin pie."

"Then," said Washerwoman Winnie, "I must make somebody else happy. I made a ginger cake this morning. Now that I have this big pumpkin pie for my Thanksgiving dinner, I don't need the cake. I will take it to the poor Pretty children. It will taste good to them." She took the cake to the poor Pretty children.

"Thank you," said the poor Pretty children, "but why did you bring the ginger cake to us?"

"Widow Lee gave me a big pumpkin pie, and I am going to have that for my dinner. I want you to have a good dinner too," said Washerwoman Winnie. "That is why I have given you my ginger cake."

"Then," said the poor Pretty children, "we must make somebody else happy. Let us

take a slice of the ginger cake to the little
lame boy that lives in the lane. It will taste
good to him." They took a slice of the ginger
cake to the little lame boy that lived in the
lane.

"Thank you," said the lame boy, "but why
did you bring a slice of your cake to me?"

"Washerwoman Winnie gave us a whole
cake," said the poor Pretty children. "We
are going to have that for our dinner and
we want you to have a good dinner too.
That is why we have given you a slice of
our cake."

"Then," said the lame boy, "I must make
somebody else happy. I will save all the
crumbs of my cake and give them to the
birds."

The lame boy saved all his crumbs and
threw them out of the window to the birds.
The birds ate them and were glad. They flew

around singing, "Peep! peep!" which was
their way of saying "thank you."

So everybody said "thank you" and everybody had a good time; and so you see that
old Gentleman Gay was right.

Said old Gentleman Gay,
"On Thanksgiving Day,
If you want a good time,
Give something away."

(Adapted from a poem by Marian Douglas)

Some
Things
to
think
about

twisted

wandered

awful

(roam)

foaming

echo

trundle

(under)

thunder

parents

WHEN THE LITTLE BOY RAN AWAY

When the little boy ran away from home,
  The birds in the tree-top knew,
And they all sang, "Stay!" but he wandered
  away
  Under the skies of blue.
And the wind came whispering from the tree,
  "Follow me, follow me!"
And it sang him a song that was soft and
  sweet

And scattered the roses before his feet
  That day, that day,
  When the little boy ran away.

The violets whispered, "Your eyes are blue
  And lovely and bright to see,
And so are mine, and I'm kin to you,
  So dwell in the light with me."
But the little boy laughed, while the wind in
  glee
Sang, "Follow, follow me!"

And the wind called the clouds from their
    home in the skies
And said to the violet, "Shut your eyes!"
    That day, that day,
    When the little boy ran away.
Then the wind played leapfrog over the hills
    And twisted each leaf and limb;
And all the rivers and all the rills
    Were foaming mad with him;

And 'twas dark as the darkest night could be,
But still came the wind's voice, "Follow me!"
And over the mountain and up from the hollow
Came echoing voices with, "Follow him; fol-
  low!"
  That awful day,
  When the little boy ran away.

Then the little boy cried, "Let me go, let
    me go!"
  For a scared, scared boy was he.
But the thunder growled from a black cloud,
    "No!"
  And the wind roared, "Follow me!"
And an old gray owl from a treetop flew,
Saying: "Who are you-oo? Who are you-oo!"
And the little boy sobbed, "I'm lost away!
And I want to go home where my parents stay."
  O, the awful day
  When the little boy ran away!

Then the moon looked out from a cloud and said:
  "Are you sorry you ran away?
If I light you home to your trundle bed,
  Will you stay, little boy, will you stay?"
And the little boy promised—and cried and
    cried—
He never would leave his mother's side,
And the moonlight led him over the plain;
And his mother welcomed him home again.
  But, O what a day
  When the little boy ran away!

moment	(rope)	sewed
quarrel	hope	hullo
country	(mean)	travel
	bean	gurgling
		alas

HOW THE BEAN GOT ITS BLACK SEAM

A TEACHER–PUPIL STORY

Teacher

Once upon a time there was a poor old woman living in a village of a far country. She had gathered some beans and was making ready to cook them. She built a fire of sticks, but as those were damp, they did not burn well. So she thrust in a handful of

dry straw. Now the flames leaped up, and the sticks snapped and crackled in the blaze.

Pupils

A live red coal flew out of the fire, fell on the ground beside a straw, and lay there smoking. Just then a bean dropped from the pot which the old woman was filling, rolled away, and came to rest close to the coal and the straw.

"Hullo, Mr. Coal," said the straw. "How

you smoke! Are you frightened? Where did
you come from?"

"I just sprang out of that fire," answered
the coal. "If I had not jumped just as I did,
I should now be nothing but ashes. My, look
at that blaze!"

"I, too, jumped in the nick of time," spoke
up the bean. "That old woman was just
putting me into the pot when I leaped out
and here I am."

"Yes, here you are, silly thing," broke out the coal and the straw together. "But what are you going to do? As soon as the old woman sees you, back you'll go into the pot, and it's hotter now than when you left it."

"Don't think about me; think of yourselves," answered the bean. "When the old woman picks me up, she'll step on you, Mr. Coal, and crush your life out. And you, Mrs. Straw, she'll stick into the blaze. It's hotter there than in the pot."

"Come, come," said the straw, softly, "let's not quarrel. Let's be friends and stick together. Perhaps we can save ourselves yet."

"You are quite right, Mrs. Straw," said the coal.

Teacher

The bean said nothing, but she listened eagerly to the plans of the two others. These

167

soon agreed to travel together to a far country, where they hoped to find their fortune.
They set out without delay, and the bean
rolled along behind.

Soon the three travellers came to a little
gurgling brook. It seemed to them a mighty
rushing and roaring torrent.

Pupils

"Oh, dear, what shall we do now?" asked the
bean, speaking for the first time since the journey
began. "We can never get across these awful
waters. What shall we do! Oh, what shall
we do!"

"Don't cry, little Bean," said the straw,
proudly. "I'll help you and Mr. Coal across
in a twinkling."

Then the straw laid herself across the
stream. She was just long enough to reach
from bank to bank.

"Now walk over the bridge, Mr. Coal and Miss Bean," called the straw.

The coal hastened on to the straw bridge while the bean stood and watched him. All went well until the coal reached the middle of the stream. Then the bridge bent so low under him and the waters thundered so loudly that the coal stopped in fright.

The coal stood still for only a moment. But, alas, that was a moment too long.

The dry straw smoked, burst into a tiny flame, and broke in two. Down fell the coal into the water below and was drowned. The burning straw bridge also fell into the water, which put out the flames, and the two pieces of straw went floating away down stream.

All this the little bean saw, watching safely from the bank. And she thought it the funniest thing that ever happened. So she laughed and she laughed—until she burst!

This would have been the end of little Miss Bean, had not a tailor passed that way just then. He was sorry for the poor bean, so he picked up the two parts tenderly, and quickly sewed them together. But the thread that he used was black. And ever since that time some beans have a black seam around them.

North   ferns   comforted
whistling   gentians

FRIENDS

North Wind came whistling through the wood
  Where the tender, sweet things grew—
The tall fair ferns and the maiden hair,
  And the gentle gentians blue.
"It's very cold! Are we growing old?"
  They sighed, "What shall we do?"
The sigh went up to the loving leaves.
  "We must help," they whispered low.
"They are frightened and weak, O brave old
    trees!
  But we love you well, you know."
And the trees said, "We are strong—make
    haste!
  Down to the darlings go."

So the leaves went floating, floating down,
  All yellow, and brown, and red,
And the frail little trembling, thankful things
  Lay still, and were comforted.
And the blue sky smiled through the bare old
  trees,
  Down on their soft warm bed.

—L. G. WARNER.

(mouth)   splendid   (mountain)
  south   fountain

HELP ONE ANOTHER

"Help one another," the snowflakes said,
As they cuddled down in their fleecy bed.
"One of us here would not be felt,
One of us here would quickly melt;
But I'll help you, and you help me,
And then what a splendid drift there'll be."

"Help one another," the maple spray
Said to its fellow leaves one day;
"The sun would wither me here alone,
Long enough ere the day is gone;
But I'll help you, and you help me,
And then what a splendid shade there'll be."

"Help one another," the dewdrop cried,
Seeing another drop close to its side;
"The warm south wind would dry me away,
And I should be gone ere noon today;
But I'll help you, and you help me,
And we'll make a brook and run to the sea."

"Help one another," a grain of sand
Said to another grain close at hand;
"The wind may carry me out to the sea,
And then, oh, what will become of me?
But come, my brother, give me your hand,
We'll build a mountain and then we will
   stand."

And so the snowflakes grew to drifts;
The grains of sand to a mountain;
The leaves became a summer shade;
The dewdrops fed a fountain.

(dart)   rule   (but)   (neither)

party   hour   shut   either

invited   counted   hedge   cherries

cuckoo   berries

THE KING OF THE BIRDS

Long, long ago when the world was new, the birds had a party. All the birds in the world were invited and I think they all came. The eagle was there and the humming bird, and all big birds and little birds. Brown birds, black birds, yellow birds came; red birds, blue birds, white birds came; birds of every other color came.

They covered every tree, bush, and bit of grass for miles and miles around. What a chattering and a chirping they made as they sat around waiting for their dinner. And what a dinner it was! There were worms and grubs of every kind. There were wheat and oats and grains of every kind. There were cherries and berries of every kind.

When they had eaten all they could, the cuckoo spoke to them.

"My friends," he said, "men have kings to rule over them. The beasts have the lion for their king. We should have a king to rule over us. Let us choose a king today."

"Yes, yes, yes," chirped all the other birds. "Let us choose a king today."

"Well," said the cuckoo, "whom shall we choose?"

"Let us choose the one who can fly highest," said the eagle, because he knew he would win.

"Yes! yes! let us choose the one who can fly highest," chirped all the other birds.

So the next day all the birds met in a big meadow. The cuckoo counted, "One, two, three!" At the word "three" all the birds flew up into the air. There were so many of them that they hid the sun.

Up, up, up they flew, but one by one the little birds grew tired and came back to the earth. At last only the eagle was to be seen flying higher and higher until he looked like a tiny, tiny speck.

But a tiny little bird without a name was hidden among the eagle's feathers. So when the eagle had left all the other birds below, the little bird without a name was still on his back.

Now, when the eagle saw that all the other

birds had given up the race, he began to come
down, too. Then the little bird without a
name came out and flew much higher than
the eagle had done.

"The eagle is king! The eagle is king!"
cried all the other birds, as the eagle came
down.

"He is not! He is not!" cried the little
bird without a name. "I flew much higher
than the eagle. I am king! I am king!"

"You cheated! You cheated!" cried the
other birds. "The race was not fair! We
won't have a little bird without a name for
our king!"

"Let us have another race," said the cuckoo.

"Yes, and we will see that it is a fair race!"

cried the other birds. "No cheating! No cheating!"

"The bird who can fall deepest into the earth shall be our king," said the duck, because she knew she would win.

"Yes! yes!" cried all the other birds.

So the birds met for another race. The duck dived under the water down, down, down. When she came up, all the other birds cried, "The duck is our king! The duck is our king!"

"No, she isn't," called the little bird without a name. "I'm away down here in a mouse's hole. I am king! I am king!"

"You are not our king. You are a cheat! a cheat!" chirped all the other birds. "We will keep you shut up in that mouse hole until you are dead."

So they told the owl to watch the hole all night long, and said, "If you let that little cheat out we will kill you."

Then all the birds flew away to their nests, for they were tired with the races.

The owl sat and stared at the hole for a long hour. Then he stared at it for another long, long hour. He had been racing, too, and was tired and sleepy.

"I'll go to sleep with one eye and watch with the other," he said. So he shut his right eye. But after a while the left eye grew so sleepy that he closed it, too, and forgot to open the right eye. And now both eyes were fast asleep.

The little bird without a name had been peeking from the mouse's hole all the time. Just as soon as he saw the owl's two eyes shut, he crept from the hole, oh, so softly.

Then away to a thick hedge he flew. When he felt safe, he cried out, "I am king! I am king!"

His loud cries woke the other birds. They

came flying from their nests. They were so angry, they would have killed the owl. But he had hidden away in a hollow tree.

From that day the owl has never dared to fly about in the daytime for fear the other birds would kill him. That is why the owl flies at night and hides in the daytime. And because a mouse made the hole that hid the little bird without a name, the owl has killed all the mice he can catch ever since.

As for the little bird without a name, he did not dare to fly about among the other birds either. He knew they would kill him for cheating. So he lived in thick hedges where the other birds could not find him; and when he saw any birds near, he called, "I am king! I am king!"

"Yes," called the other birds, "you are king! A great king! A king that has to hide in thick hedges! So the birds gave the little bird without a name, the name of "Hedge king," which means the same as wren; and "wren" he is called to this very day.

With our Feathered Friends

(girl)	(sea)	(cane)
whirl	reason	vane
point	heavy	else
waul		perch

THE DROWNING OF MR. LEGHORN

A TEACHER–PUPIL STORY

Teacher

One day Mr. Leghorn, the rooster, and Mrs. Leghorn, the hen, were out walking.

They came to a wide, deep brook. Mrs. Leghorn, who was light and quick, flew safely across; but Mr. Leghorn, who was heavy and slow, fell, splash! into the water.

Pupils

Mrs. Leghorn was sure Mr. Leghorn was drowned. So, without turning to see, she flew screaming and cackling toward the farmyard.

"What does ail you, Mrs. Leghorn? Why are you screaming and cackling so loudly?" asked the Wind-Mill as Mrs. Leghorn flew past.

"Mr. Leghorn has fallen into the brook and is drowned. That's why I am screaming and cackling so loudly," replied Mrs. Leghorn.

"What a pity! I'll swing my arms and creak. That's the best I can do for poor Mr. Leghorn." And the Wind-Mill fell to swinging his arms and creaking with all his might.

186

When the Big Barn Door heard the Wind-Mill creaking and saw him swinging his long arms, he called out, "What ails you, Wind-Mill? Why do you swing your arms and creak so?"

"Why, Mr. Leghorn has fallen into the brook and is drowned, and Mrs. Leghorn is screaming and cackling. That's why I swing my arms and creak," answered the Wind-Mill.

187

"Poor Mr. Leghorn, poor Mrs. Leghorn!" said the Big Barn Door. "I'll slam and bang. That's the best I can do." And the Big Barn Door fell to slamming and banging with all his might.

The Old Red Ox heard the Big Barn Door slamming and banging, and cried out, "O, Big Barn Door, why are you slamming and banging so?"

"Reason enough," answered the Big Barn Door. "Mr. Leghorn has fallen into the brook and is drowned; Mrs. Leghorn is screaming and cackling; and Wind-Mill is swinging his arms

and creaking. That's why I am slamming and banging so."

"How sorry I am," said the Old Red Ox. "I'll paw the ground and bellow. What else can I do?" And he fell to pawing and bellowing with all his might.

"What is the matter, Old Red Ox?" asked the Watch Dog. "Why are you pawing and bellowing so?"

"Matter enough," answered the Old Red Ox. "Mr. Leghorn has fallen into the brook and is drowned; Mrs. Leghorn is screaming and cackling; Wind-Mill is swinging his arms and creaking; and Big Barn Door is slamming and banging. That's why I am pawing and bellowing so."

"O dear me," said the Watch Dog. "I'll bark and whine. That's all I can do." And

he fell to barking and whining with all his might.

The Old Gray Horse heard the Watch Dog barking and whining, and said, "What is the matter with you, Watch Dog? Why do you bark and whine so?"

"Wouldn't you bark and whine if you could?" answered the Watch Dog. "Mr. Leghorn has fallen into the brook and is drowned; Mrs. Leghorn is screaming and cackling; Wind-Mill is swinging his arms and creaking; the Big Barn Door is slamming and banging; and the Old Red Ox is pawing and bellowing. That's why I am barking and whining."

"The poor things!" said Old Gray Horse. "I'll prance and neigh. What more can I do?" And he fell to prancing and neighing with all his might.

Pupils

The Weather-Vane looked down from his high perch and saw the Old Gray Horse prancing and neighing. "What's the trouble, Old Gray Horse?" he called out. "Why are you prancing and neighing so?"

191

"Trouble indeed," answered the Old Gray Horse. "Mr. Leghorn has fallen into the brook and is drowned; Mrs. Leghorn is screaming and cackling; Wind-mill is swinging his arms and creaking; the Big Barn Door is slamming and banging; the Old Red Ox is pawing and bellowing; and the Watch-Dog is barking and whining. That's why I am prancing and neighing so."

"O dear, O dear," said the Weather-Vane, "what shall I do? I'll whirl and point. That's all I can do." And he fell to whirling and pointing with all his might.

Pussy Cat looked up and saw Weather-Vane whirling and pointing. "O, Weather-Vane," she cried out. "Why do you whirl and point so?"

"Because I can do nothing else," answered the Weather-Vane. "Mr. Leghorn has fallen into the brook and is drowned; Mrs. Leghorn is screaming and cackling; Wind-Mill is swinging his arms and creaking; the Big Barn Door is slamming and banging; the Old Red Ox is pawing and bellowing; the Watch Dog is barking and whining; and the Old Gray Horse is prancing and neighing. That's why I am whirling and pointing so."

Teacher

"O, how sad!" said Pussy Cat. "I'll waul and squall. That's the best I can do." And she fell to wauling and squalling with all her might.

At this moment, when Pussy Cat was wauling and squalling, when the Weather-Vane was whirling and pointing, when the Old Gray Horse was prancing and neighing, when the Watch Dog was barking and whining, when the Old Red Ox was pawing and bellowing, when the Big Barn Door was slamming and

193

banging, when the Wind-Mill was swinging his arms and creaking, when Mrs. Leghorn was screaming and cackling, Mr. Leghorn flew to the highest rail on the fence and crew,

"Cock-a-doodle-doo,
What's the matter with you?"

seized   stretched   bunch

bundle   offering   easy

basket   fiercely   own

saucer   faintly

THE STARVING OF MRS. LEGHORN

Mr. and Mrs. Leghorn often went nutting. Mr. Leghorn was very polite and kind to Mrs. Leghorn. He ran about searching everywhere for nuts.

When he found a nut he would call to Mrs. Leghorn, who would hasten to him. Then he would pick up the nut, roll it over and over, lay it down, and pick it up again and again, all the time telling Mrs. Leghorn what a very nice nut that was, what a good hen she was, and how smart he was to find nuts for her.

At last he would drop the nut before Mrs. Leghorn. She would peck it once or twice to make sure that all that Mr. Leghorn had said of it was true. Then the greedy hen would swallow the nut whole, without once offering to share it with Mr. Leghorn, and without saying, "Thank you."

One day Mr. Leghorn found a very large nut, the largest nut he had ever seen. How proudly he called to Mrs. Leghorn! It took him a long time to tell all about that big nut and how he had found it, and to brag about his own smartness. But after a time he gave the nut to Mrs. Leghorn. The greedy hen seized the nut to swallow it, but—it wouldn't go down! She tried again and again, she opened her beak wider and wider, but it was no use. The nut was too large.

Mr. Leghorn, who had been watching Mrs. Leghorn trying to swallow the big nut cried, "O, my poor Mrs. Leghorn, what shall I do? You can't eat that nut; you'll surely starve. What shall I do?"

"Run and ask Mr. Wise Owl," said Mrs. Leghorn. "He can tell us what to do."

So away ran Mr. Leghorn to the Wise Owl, screaming with all his might.

"O, Mr. Wise Owl," he cried, my poor Mrs. Leghorn is starving. She can't swallow the big nut. What shall I do?"

"Who, who, who?" hooted the Wise Owl, blinking his great round eyes.

"Mrs. Leghorn, my Mrs. Leghorn, my own dear Mrs. Leghorn," screamed Mr. Leghorn

"She can't swallow the big nut. She will starve. Can you tell me what to do?"

Mr. Wise Owl stared straight ahead a moment—it seemed an age to Mr. Leghorn—then answered slowly, "Yes, Mr. Leghorn, I can tell you what to do. But you must first bring me a mouse."

Away rushed Mr. Leghorn to Pussy Cat. "My good Miss Pussy Cat," he cried, "dear

Mrs. Leghorn is starving. Will you please catch me a mouse? I want it to take to Mr. Wise Owl, who is going to tell me what to do."

"Yes, Mr. Leghorn," answered Pussy Cat,

'I will catch you a mouse, but you must first bring me a saucer of milk."

Off flew Mr. Leghorn to Mrs. Mooly Cow. "Dear, kind Mrs. Mooly Cow," he said, "poor Mrs. Leghorn is starving. Will you please give me a saucer of milk? I want it to take to Miss Pussy Cat, who is going to catch me a mouse for Mr. Wise Owl, who is going to tell me what to do."

"Yes, Mr. Leghorn," answered Mrs. Mooly

Cow, "I will give you a saucer of milk, but you must first bring me a bundle of corn."

Away sped Mr. Leghorn to the Farmer.

"O, Mr. Farmer," said Mr. Leghorn, "Mrs. Leghorn is starving. Please will you be so kind as to cut me a bundle of corn? I want it to take to Mrs. Mooly Cow, who is going to give me a saucer of milk for Miss Pussy Cat, who is going to catch me a mouse for Mr. Wise Owl, who is going to tell me what to do."

"Yes, indeed, Mr. Leghorn," said the Farmer, "I will cut you a bundle of corn, but you must first bring me a new coat."

Off hastened Mr. Leghorn to the Tailor.

"O, Mr. Tailor," cried Mr. Leghorn, "Mrs. Leghorn is starving. Won't you please give me a new coat? I want it to take to Mr. Farmer, who is going to cut me a bundle of corn for Mrs. Mooly Cow, who is going to

give me a saucer of milk for Miss Pussy Cat,
who is going to catch me a mouse for Mr.
Wise Owl, who is going to tell me what to do."

"Yes, Mr. Leghorn," answered Mr. Tailor,
"I shall be very glad to give you a new coat,
but you must first bring me a pound of wool."

Away hurried Mr. Leghorn to Mrs. Sheep.

"O, good Mrs. Sheep," he said, "Mrs.
Leghorn is starving. Do, please, give me a
pound of wool. I want it to take to Mr.
Tailor, who is going to give me a new coat

for Mr. Farmer, who is going to cut me a bundle of corn for Mrs. Mooly Cow, who is going to give me a saucer of milk for Miss Pussy Cat, who is going to catch me a mouse for Mr. Wise Owl, who is going to tell me what to do."

"To be sure, Mr. Leghorn," said Mrs. Sheep, "I will give you a pound of wool, but you must first bring me a bunch of clover."

Away ran Mr. Leghorn to the Farmer's
Wife.

"O, good, kind Farmer's Wife," cried Mr.
Leghorn, "Mrs. Leghorn is starving. Won't
you, please, pull me a bunch of clover? I
want it to take to Mrs. Sheep, who is going
to give me a pound of wool for Mr. Tailor,
who is going to give me a new coat for Mr.
Farmer, who is going to cut me a bundle of

corn for Mrs. Mooly Cow, who is going to give me a saucer of milk for Miss Pussy Cat, who is going to catch me a mouse for Mr. Wise Owl, who is going to tell me what to do."

"Yes, yes," answered the kind Farmer's Wife, "I will gladly pull you a bunch of clover, but you must first bring me a dozen eggs."

Mr. Leghorn fairly flew back to Mrs. Leghorn, who was still trying to swallow the large nut. He seemed to forget all his politeness.

"Where's your nest, Mrs. Leghorn? where's your nest? Tell me this instant!" he screamed.

Mrs. Leghorn had never told any one where her nest was. That was her secret; and she would not have told her secret now — not even to keep herself from starving — but Mr. Leghorn looked so angry that she became frightened. She thought he had gone mad and would hurt her. So she answered faintly,

205

"Under the corner of the barn."

Away to the corner of the barn rushed Mr. Leghorn, where he found Mrs. Leghorn's nest full of eggs. He took a dozen in a basket and hurried off to the Farmer's Wife, who pulled him a bunch of clover, which he carried to Mrs. Sheep, who gave him a pound of wool, which he took to Mr. Tailor, who gave him a new coat, which he brought to Mr. Farmer, who cut him a bundle of corn, which he carried to Mrs. Mooly Cow, who gave him a saucer of milk, which he took to Miss Pussy Cat, who caught him a mouse, which he carried to Mr. Wise Owl.

"There, Mr. Wise Owl," cried Mr. Leghorn, quite out of breath, "there's a nice fat mouse. Now tell me what I shall do for poor Mrs. Leghorn, who is starving because she can't swallow the big nut."

"Who, who, who?" cried Mr. Wise Owl, staring sleepily at the fat mouse.

"Mrs. Leghorn, she is starving!" screamed Mr. Leghorn, now quite angry. "She can't swallow the big nut. You said you would tell me what to do.

"O, yes," said Mr. Wise Owl, "to be sure, that's easy. Just go and find Mrs. Leghorn some smaller nuts that she can swallow, and eat the big one yourself."

crickets   (past)   (feel)

ocean   master   heel

chasing   beyond   (own)

urged   (child)   unknown

scarcely   wildly   afternoon

MR. AND MRS. LEGHORN TO THE RESCUE

A TEACHER–PUPIL STORY

Teacher

Mr. and Mrs. Leghorn went for a stroll one afternoon. They had never been far from home and they soon came into unknown places. But they wandered on and on, chasing grasshoppers and crickets, and now and then stopping to scratch for a worm,

until they finally came to the bank of a frog
pond.

Pupils

"Look, Mrs. Leghorn," said Mr. Leghorn,
"there's the ocean, the wide, blue ocean that
we have heard so much about."

"Indeed it is," answered Mrs. Leghorn.
"Could you believe we had come so far!"

Splash! . . . *Splash!*

"What was that?" cried Mrs. Leghorn.

"What was that?" cried Mr. Leghorn.

209

Teacher

"Help me out! Help me out!" came a deep voice from the pond.

"Me, too! Me, too!" came a little, peeping voice from the same place.

Pupils

"Why, that's our good master and his little boy," cried Mr. and Mrs. Leghorn together. "They've fallen into the ocean!"

"Help me out! Help me out! Me, too! Me, too!" came again from the pond.

"Yes, good Master, yes," screamed Mr. Leghorn, "We'll help you. But what shall we do?"

"Bring a rope! A rope!" came the answer.

"A rope, a rope!" cried Mr. Leghorn. "O, where shall we find one?"

"Just beyond! Just beyond!"

Mr. Leghorn ran wildly along the bank

with Mrs. Leghorn following close on his
heels. They looked to the right, and they
looked to the left; they looked up, and
they looked down; but no rope could they
see.

"Hurry up! Hurry up!" came from the
water.

"O dear, O dear!" cried Mrs. Leghorn.

"O, where is that rope?" cried Mr. Leghorn.

"Follow your nose! Follow your nose!"
came the voice.

At that, Mr. Leghorn flew along faster
than ever. Mrs. Leghorn could hardly keep
in sight of him. But no rope could they
find.

Teacher

"Hurry up! Hurry up!" came from the
pond and urged them on, whenever they began to slacken their pace.

211

"Going down! Going down!" came the **deep** voice.

"Me, too! Me, too!" came the peeping voice.

"O, they are drowning, they are drowning!" screamed Mr. and Mrs. Leghorn.

"Let 'em drown! Let 'em drown!" came the voice.

"What!" cried Mr. Leghorn.

"What!" cried Mrs. Leghorn.

"Better go home! Better go home!" called the deep voice.

Mr. and Mrs. Leghorn stood staring at each other. They could scarcely believe their ears.

"Go to roost! Go to roost!" came the voice.

Mr. and Mrs. Leghorn began to look silly. The sun had set and it was growing dark. They turned about and started off homeward.

"You're fooled! You're fooled!" sounded after them as they left the banks of the pond.

"He told the truth that time, even if he is only a frog," said Mrs. Leghorn.

VOCABULARY

Most of the words used in the preceding books of the Aldine Series are used frequently in this book. They are not listed in this vocabulary, however; here are given only the words used for the first time in this book. The number at the left of a word refers to the page on which the story begins in which that word is first used. New words are listed in the text immediately before the lesson in which they are first used.

A

15. afraid
208. afternoon
164. alas
20. among
159. awful

B

104. ballad
30. bank
195. basket
164. bean
40. bear ·
25. begged
35. believe
40. bellow
175. berries
208. beyond
107. bottom
65. branches
93. bravely
81. breathe
40. breathes
118. breezes
51. brother
107. build
195. bunch
195. bundle
40. burrowed
129. bush
57. buy

C

40. cage
78. cap
51. cave
208. chasing
175. cherries
30. chick
30. chicken
129. chirped
9. choose
129. clever
40. climbed
138. cloak
86. close
67. clothes
57. cob
93. color
171. comforted
175. counted
164. country
51. coward

215

216

218

219

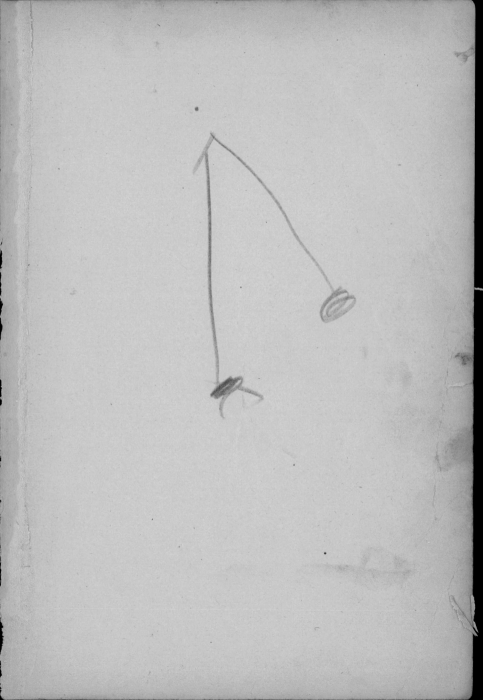